IT'S ONLY A GAME

Tony Husband

ARCTURUS

For Carole

The cartoons on pages 7, 20, 22, 79, 105 and 148 are reproduced by kind permission of *PRIVATE EYE* magazine / Tony Husband.

This edition published in 2012 by Arcturus Publishing Limited
26/27 Bickels Yard, 151–153 Bermondsey Street,
London SE1 3HA

Design copyright © 2012 Arcturus Publishing Limited
Image copyright © 2012 Tony Husband (except where otherwise indicated)
Introduction © 2012 Griff Rhys Jones

ISBN: 978-1-84858-932-2
AD002508EN

Printed in Malaysia

'One of the few good things about being unemployed in the 1980s was waiting for a fortnightly fix of Tony Husband's *Yobs*... classic cartooning. He's a northern treasure.'

Christopher Eccleston, actor

· ·

'Tony is the Jimi Hendrix of cartooning.'

Clive Goddard, cartoonist

· ·

'Men of Tony's unique and uncompromising vision come along once every ten thousand years. They are never simply "born". They are the result of an asteroid collision in the heavens or they are found curled up in an oyster as they tread the razor's edge between myth and legend and bewildering genius. Tony himself oozed out of a phoenix. I thank Jesus I was alive in his time.'

Guy Garvey, *Elbow*

· ·

'Tony Husband's jokes make my socks look like budgerigars.'

Terry Jones, *Monty Python*

· ·

'Over the last 30 years, it's safe to say he's made me laugh out loud more than anybody else... he comes from a dark, twisted place.'

Marc Riley, BBC 6 Music

THE 'IT' FACTOR

When I used to hang around in London's infamous Groucho Club with Tony Husband, he was always popping off upstairs 'just to finish a cartoon'. Can you imagine? He had joke deadlines and daily comic turnarounds, and end-of-the week agendas, and editors drumming their fingers on the tables, even while he was sitting on some grubby sofa waiting for something to happen. (That is all anyone ever does in the Groucho Club.) This was because he works in the newspaper or printed media business, which pays badly and treats its staff like bees.

So he would knock off a few cartoons, follow a routine, get some jokes down and get a reaction, and then draw them up, have a few beers, and then do a strip cartoon or two, then have a burger and then go on to a party and then draw some more jokes. It all seemed terrifying – tied to a ferris wheel of comic inspiration.

'More of your funniest jokes, Tony!', 'Make sure you give us some very humorous pocket cartoons by six o'clock this evening, Tony', 'Come on, Tony, you are under contract to be funny. Produce!' So he did. Still does. Rather too easily and brilliantly if you ask me. Not any old clichéd gags, but new, laugh aloud, right on the edge of complaints to the letters page of *Private Eye* stuff, plus amusing drawings too, and quite sexy ones as well. (How does he make you fancy a couple of pin legs and some balloon breasts? It's all very mysterious.) Prolific, and yet I never saw him worry about it. This wouldn't be of any note at all, except that he did worry about everything else: his dog and his house and his train and his beer and comedian Rory McGrath, for some reason. Mr Husband is endearing. He is a quietly lugubrious big bloke, of a northern nature and fretful too.

But he never fretted about jokes. In fact when I quizzed him he chuckled in an assured manner and let his eyelids drop to 'knowing' mode. 'Well, as McLachlan said,' he told me, 'you've either got it, or you haven't.' And of course, he knew that he had. He sits down and picks up a pen and there is a comic vision of the world – that's what he's got. He has 'it'.

Mind you, he asked me to write this knowing I despise organised sport. I don't play golf, have only once attended a football match, never watch darts, don't understand the rules of rugby and amused Rory McGrath by not knowing what the Emirates Stadium was. This is another of Tony's jokes. But there we go. Thanks. I get the references. I get the attitude. I don't care about the subject matter here. I still find it funny. I suppose that's 'it'.

Griff Rhys Jones

'He has a tendency to exaggerate.'

'I said no rude words, Harold.'

'He's fielding very silly mid off.'

'Erm, excuse me... did he mention the putter I lent him?'

'Mum... dad's watching beach volleyball again!'

'How can you tell which one is Wayne Rooney's baby?'

'Excuse me, we don't have replay... Was that out?'

'His grip's all wrong? He's only 18 months old for heaven's sake.'

'Anything biting?'

'If I had my way, they'd do away with matches and just have penalties.'

'Not sure that's what they meant by sexy cricket.'

'Well, that's me sorted for the World Cup.'

'Why are we laughing? Erm... I filmed your swing on my mobile and was just showing the lads.'

'Perhaps you should work on your legs a bit.'

'Isn't there a game we could both play, Keith?'

'I love our baby racing days.'

'Michael, do I have to keep reminding you I'm too old to take up the trapeze?'

'Your cat keeps doing its business on our bowling green.'

'Stop moaning, Riley, you're lucky to have a job.'

'Why does everyone have a go at Audley Harrison? He's never hurt anyone!'

'This new 3D television is very good, isn't it, Gerald?'

'Did anyone tell the keeper the game has been abandoned?'

'<u>You</u> ask her about her gender.'

'Gymnastics is on.'

'Have you seen the wheels on Hamilton's car?'

'I find Ryan Giggs really inspiring.'

'OK, besides centre–forward, what's your favourite position?'

'Oh... er, thank you very much.'

'Doesn't he look different on television?'

'Yes, it is an unusual putting style, but it works for him.'

'Charles is crazy about golf. He bought the lamp-post Tiger Woods crashed into on eBay.'

'Can't say the linesman is filling me with confidence.'

'You're right, there is someone still out there.'

'They only let him out once the whistle blows.'

'By the look of things, you've got him on the ropes.'

'The transfer window is madness. I don't know how but
I've just sold my wife to Leicester City.'

'Thomas, do you realise you're a big disappointment to your father?'

'The referee is out now inspecting the pitch.'

'Sometimes I think you love United more than you love me... I said... '

'No, you go and get the ball.'

'Don't know about you, but I can't say I've done much training for this.'

'He was caught in the clubhouse wearing spikes.'

'Bad news. I've had to sell your car to pay for my season ticket.'

'He likes to feel part of the Grand National.'

'OK, we've got until Wimbledon finishes.'

'Oops...!!'

'Please don't leave, darling... how will I manage without you?'

'I'm the boss, so if I want my PA to caddie for me she will.'

'My goodness, Boscombe, have you seen this?'

'Look at the state of you... why can't you
stay in and play computer games like other kids?'

'Umpire? No, we couldn't get a babysitter.'

'I'd heard he was a bad loser but he took it quite well.'

THE SCREAM
ANDY MURRAY

'He was useless as a mascot, so we had an idea... '

'Your team has a reputation for, er, being a bit physical... How do you respond to that?'

'Well, there is a local rule about being eaten by a lion.'

'All this talk about unrest in the dressing room is ridiculous.'

'Do you fancy playing a round?'

'Can you ring back? He's pretending to be a windsurfer.'

'Not tonight, darling. I'm playing 18 holes first thing.'

'Fast, isn't he?'

'It's the new referees kit.'

'Schumacher's back, so you're driving one of these.'

The man who turned down a beer in a rugby club bar.

'He's been under a lot of strain lately.'

'We put clingfilm between the posts.'

'No, it's Mick's got an eagle, not an eagle's got Mick.'

82

'I told you it was a mistake playing golf with your mother.'

'Someone was talking about the recession. What's a recession?'

'Blow!!!'

'Can you keep it down? He's going for the pin.'

'Looks as though we might not be the first team he's played for.'

'Sigh... I see his trampoline's fixed.'

'Who will we boo now Ronaldo's not in the Premiership?'

'Our marriage is going through a rough patch.'

'Apparently, they're friends of your father's from the golf club.'

'Five quid on me losing all my money by the end of the day.'

'Choose a card, any card.'

'That team of salesmen are hot. They just sold me a driver I don't need.'

'Do you ever like to pretend you're at the Velodrome?'

'The new foreign owner's here to see you.'

'There's no one up ahead. It's kind of eerie...'

'And remember, there's always someone worse off than you.'

'We're trying to speed him up for the Olympics.'

'He's a bit of a prodigy.'

'I'm calling an impromptu board meeting.
Is this a five- or a six-iron?'

'So I'm at the crease, three balls left, six runs needed... What should I do?'

'So you'll be driving 60 yards now.'

'Now that's what you call a late tackle.'

'Huh, they take two inches off a jump and expect you to be grateful.'

'You really get carried away with the sailing on the telly, don't you, Jim?'

'I didn't touch him.'

'Do we have to applaud every time the boss hits a good shot?'

'Ah, the romance of Manchester on a Wednesday night... '

'See you down there.'

'Shall I turn it down a little?'

'Erm... you are remembering this is just a friendly?'

'If I was you, I'd declare the ball lost.'

The split second after you realise you forgot to put your protector on...

'C'mon, Sir Alex, you can do it... it's not hard to apologise!'

'It doesn't look like they're going to give us much of a game.'

THE PENALTY

AN ENGLISHMAN'S VIEW

'If you ask me, you get too tense on these occasions.'

'I see Joey Barton's back in training.'

'His style is primitive but effective.'

Football's top assembly line...

'Tell the chairman to close the transfer window, there's a hell of an overdraft.'

'The Oxford team is definitely heavier.'

'I bet he's on drugs.'

'We've got someone to mark Peter Crouch.'

'Could you breathe into this please, sir?'

'That's the first time this season they've shown any fight.'

'Excuse me, lads, can we have a moment's silence?
They'll be burying the mother-in-law about now.'

'Of course, we'll get away with it, just don't panic.'

'My art is inspired by football: I call this one Heurelho Gomes.'

'Miss Etheridge, take a putt for me, will you?'

'Half an hour ago they were rubbish.'

'Can you lot shut up? The wife's got a headache.'

'... and we have a wonderful crèche system.'

OLYMPIC
TICKETS
TO PAY
FOR

TA

'Tell me, Grandad, about when sport was fun.'

'And how long have you had the yips?'

'I'm bored, Mary-Lou, buy me one of those Limey soccer franchises.'

'All right, Roberts, you want my job, come and get it.'

'Get on with it, man. It's only the monthly medal.'

'Don't be silly, George, go and do the dishes.'

'I think my husband suspects.'

How banter used to be.

'Oxygen mask? No, it's my box, darling.'

'Once upon a time there was a great football team... '

'I'm thinking of joining a gym.'

"'Scuse me, can we, er, play through?'

'Rooney, you're fat and useless!'

'This is where we practise diving.'